Ted and Ned Get Wet

By Steve Metzger Illustrated by Jim Paillot

SCHOLASTIC INC.
New York Toronto London Auckland Sydney
Mexico City New Delhi Hong Kong Buenos Aires

P9-DGI-890

There is Ted.

There is Ned.

3

There is Ed.

Ted and Ned get out of bed.

Ted and Ned bend.

Let's get wet!

7

Not yet!

Get set, go!

Ned and Ted fly like jets!

Time for lunch. Ted led.

Then Ned led.

Oh, no. Ed's leg is bent!

Get the vet.

All set.

Ted and Ned went to bed.
Zzzzzz!